WHERE ARE THEY?

LOOK FOR LAURA

By
Anthony Tallarico

Copyright © 1990 Kidsbooks, Inc. and Anthony Tallarico
7004 N. California Ave.
Chicago, Ill. 60645

ISBN: 0-942025-77-6

Laura lives on a planet called MAXX. One day she decided to visit her grandmother in her astro-ferry. All her friends came to say good-bye.

LOOK FOR LAURA ON THE PLANET MAXX AND...

- ☐ Balloons (3)
- ☐ Birdhouse
- ☐ Birds (2)
- ☐ Books (3)
- ☐ Clipboard
- ☐ Clocks (4)
- ☐ Coffeepot
- ☐ Covered wagon
- ☐ Dog
- ☐ Elephant
- ☐ Evergreen tree
- ☐ Fish
- ☐ Flowerpot
- ☐ Footballs (2)
- ☐ Fork
- ☐ Graduate
- ☐ Hamburger
- ☐ Hot dog
- ☐ Ice-cream pop
- ☐ Jump rope
- ☐ Kite
- ☐ Old radio
- ☐ Old tire
- ☐ Pizza
- ☐ Sled
- ☐ Tepee
- ☐ Train engine
- ☐ Turtle
- ☐ TV set
- ☐ Umbrella

But when Laura got into the astro-ferry, she pressed the wrong button.

Suddenly she was in an alien world surrounded by strange-looking creatures. Everything was wet! This wasn't her grandmother's house. This wasn't MAXX. This wasn't even land!

LOOK FOR LAURA IN THE OCEAN AND...

☐ Anchovy
☐ Bats (2)
☐ Bell
☐ Books (2)
☐ Bow
☐ Cheese
☐ Crown
☐ Cup
☐ Fire hydrant
☐ Flowers (2)
☐ Ghost
☐ Guitar
☐ Hammer
☐ Haystack
☐ Heart
☐ Horseshoe
☐ Ice-cream cone
☐ Key
☐ Mermaid
☐ Needlefish
☐ Octopus
☐ Old tire
☐ Pencil
☐ Pizza
☐ Saw
☐ Seesaw
☐ Snail
☐ Straw hat
☐ Telescope
☐ Treasure chest
☐ Turtles (3)
☐ TV set
☐ Umbrella

Laura zoomed up and finally landed...

...in a jungle watering hole. There the creatures were furry and feathery.

LOOK FOR LAURA AT THE WATERING HOLE AND...

- ☐ Arrow
- ☐ Balloons (3)
- ☐ Beach ball
- ☐ Birdbath
- ☐ Bird's nest
- ☐ Boat
- ☐ Bones (3)
- ☐ Camel
- ☐ Camera
- ☐ Crocodile
- ☐ Donkey
- ☐ Feather
- ☐ Football
- ☐ Giraffe
- ☐ Heart
- ☐ Jack-o'-lantern
- ☐ Joe of the jungle
- ☐ Lion
- ☐ Lollipop
- ☐ Owl
- ☐ Pelican
- ☐ Periscope
- ☐ Pig
- ☐ Rooster
- ☐ Snake
- ☐ Socks (2)
- ☐ Tin can
- ☐ Toucan
- ☐ Unicorn
- ☐ Wart hog
- ☐ Wolf
- ☐ Worm
- ☐ Yo-yo

But Laura wasn't sure if they were all friendly, so she got back on board and decided to explore the rest of this strange world.

As Laura flew through the sky, she saw some mountains covered with white stuff. Laura landed and for the very first time she saw—SNOW! This was fun! She wished her friends on MAXX could see the snow too.

LOOK FOR LAURA ON A SKI SLOPE IN THE ALPS AND...

- ☐ Alligator
- ☐ Artist
- ☐ Automobile
- ☐ Boat
- ☐ Bone
- ☐ Bunny
- ☐ Camel
- ☐ Cold telephone
- ☐ Dog
- ☐ Elf
- ☐ Evergreen tree
- ☐ Fish
- ☐ Football player
- ☐ Hammock
- ☐ Igloo
- ☐ Jack-o'-lantern
- ☐ Kite
- ☐ Mailbox
- ☐ Mouse
- ☐ Rake
- ☐ Santa Claus
- ☐ Scuba diver
- ☐ Skateboard
- ☐ Sleeping monster
- ☐ Snowman
- ☐ Sunglasses
- ☐ Top hat
- ☐ Turtle
- ☐ TV antenna
- ☐ Uphill skier

Then she was frightened by a loud yodel and away she went.

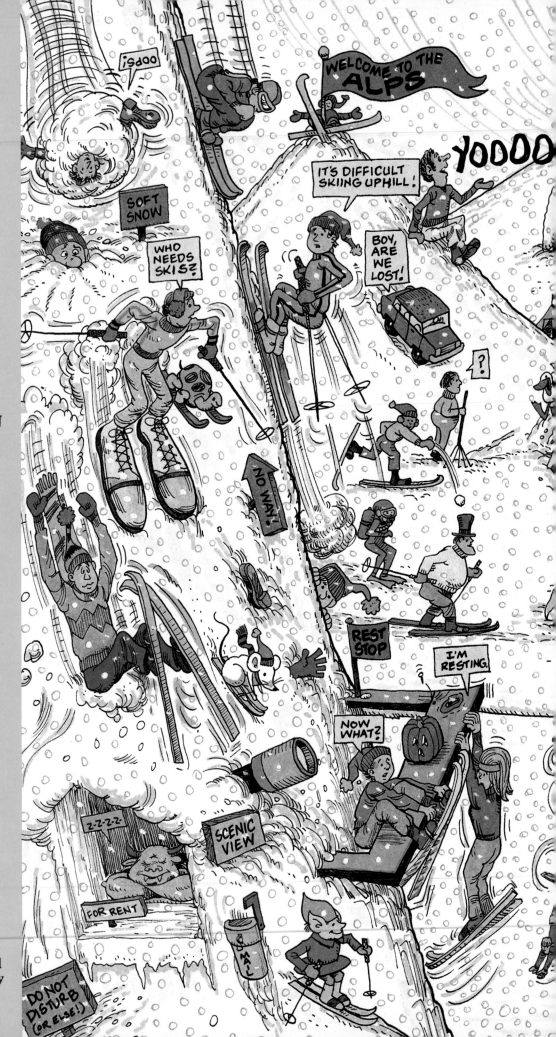

Laura flew south and landed in the desert—or rather, an oasis in the desert. Wow, it was hot! And people had towels on their heads! Everyone was too busy buying and selling at the bazaar to notice Laura, so she continued on her journey.

LOOK FOR LAURA AT THE BAH-HA BAZAAR AND...

- ☐ Beach ball
- ☐ Bird
- ☐ Broom
- ☐ Cat
- ☐ Clouds (2)
- ☐ Coconuts (4)
- ☐ Dog
- ☐ Donkey
- ☐ Elephant
- ☐ Flying carpets (2)
- ☐ Football
- ☐ Genie
- ☐ Horn
- ☐ Ice-cream cone
- ☐ Igloo
- ☐ Kite
- ☐ Necklace
- ☐ Oil well
- ☐ Pillow fight
- ☐ Rabbit
- ☐ Shovel
- ☐ Skier
- ☐ Sled
- ☐ Snail
- ☐ Snakes (4)
- ☐ Straw baskets (2)
- ☐ Sunglasses
- ☐ Telescope
- ☐ Tents (4)
- ☐ Truck
- ☐ Turtle
- ☐ Umbrella

Back north went the astro-ferry. Laura saw many beautiful places as she flew over Europe, so she decided to visit them.

LOOK FOR LAURA IN EUROPE AND...

- ☐ Automobiles (2)
- ☐ Ball
- ☐ Ballerinas (2)
- ☐ Boats (3)
- ☐ Cancan dancers
- ☐ Castle
- ☐ Dog
- ☐ Donkey
- ☐ Egret
- ☐ Fisherman
- ☐ Flying fish
- ☐ Ghost
- ☐ Gondola
- ☐ Hot-air balloon
- ☐ King
- ☐ Knight in armor
- ☐ Non-flying fish (3)
- ☐ Periscope
- ☐ Reindeer
- ☐ Skier
- ☐ Snake
- ☐ Snowmen (2)
- ☐ Starfish
- ☐ Stork
- ☐ Telescope
- ☐ Tour bus
- ☐ Train
- ☐ Tulips
- ☐ Turtle
- ☐ Windmill

Laura was beginning to get homesick and she wondered how she would find her way back to MAXX.

From the astro-ferry, Laura spotted a large group of children doing different activities. Maybe they could help.

LOOK FOR LAURA AT SUMMER CAMP AND...

☐ Alligator
☐ Basket
☐ Bats (2)
☐ Bear
☐ Broom
☐ Candy cane
☐ Cannon
☐ Cheese
☐ Cooks (2)
☐ Duck
☐ Firefighter
☐ Fish
☐ Head of a monster
☐ Headless monster
☐ Jack-o'-lantern
☐ Lake
☐ Lamp
☐ Motorcycle
☐ Owl
☐ Paper airplane
☐ Pizza
☐ Scarecrow
☐ Shovel
☐ Skateboard
☐ Skulls (2)
☐ Stepladder
☐ Target
☐ Telephone
☐ Three-legged chair
☐ Tin can
☐ Toy duck
☐ Wagon
☐ Witch

Laura had never seen so many strange activities. And no one had ever heard of the planet, MAXX.

The kids at camp directed Laura to a huge tent down the road. In the center of the tent, silly people, and animals too, seemed to be having fun.

LOOK FOR LAURA AT THE CIRCUS AND...

- ☐ Bad juggler
- ☐ Banana peel
- ☐ Binoculars
- ☐ Bowling ball
- ☐ Bow tie
- ☐ Cactus
- ☐ Cheese
- ☐ Cowboy hats (2)
- ☐ Dry paint
- ☐ Elephants (2)
- ☐ Ghost
- ☐ Hot dog
- ☐ Ice-cream cone
- ☐ Knight in armor
- ☐ Lion
- ☐ Lost shoe
- ☐ Monkey suit
- ☐ Mouse
- ☐ Picture frame
- ☐ Pie
- ☐ Pig
- ☐ Pirate
- ☐ Shoe shine box
- ☐ Skateboards (3)
- ☐ Top hat
- ☐ Training wheels
- ☐ Umbrella
- ☐ Walking flower
- ☐ Watering can

Laura enjoyed herself at the circus, but she was worried about getting home.

She tried again to get the astro-ferry to head for MAXX. Instead, she landed in a noisy city. Laura was about to give up hope of ever returning home. Then she saw some beings that looked a little like herself.

LOOK FOR LAURA IN WASHINGTON D.C. AND...

Perhaps they could help her, so she followed them as they walked...

...back to school! In the classroom, Laura watched the children do their spelling lessons. H-O-M-E spelled home.

LOOK FOR LAURA AT SCHOOL AND...

- ☐ Alexander
- ☐ Bat
- ☐ Bells (2)
- ☐ Broom
- ☐ Bubble gum
- ☐ Cat
- ☐ Clothespin
- ☐ Cupcake
- ☐ Drummer
- ☐ Easel
- ☐ Fish (2)
- ☐ Footballs (2)
- ☐ Globe
- ☐ Golf club
- ☐ Half moon
- ☐ Happy face
- ☐ Hats (2)
- ☐ Heart
- ☐ Hourglass
- ☐ Igloo
- ☐ Jump rope
- ☐ Monster mask
- ☐ Owl
- ☐ Paintbrush
- ☐ Pinocchio
- ☐ Plate
- ☐ Protoceratops
- ☐ Robin
- ☐ Robot
- ☐ School bags (2)
- ☐ Scissors
- ☐ Snow
- ☐ Soccer ball
- ☐ Stocking
- ☐ Sunglasses
- ☐ Wastepaper basket

Suddenly, Laura decided to type "M-A-X-X" in the astro-ferry's computer.

It worked! The astro-ferry zoomed home! Everyone was gathered to welcome her back to MAXX. Laura told them all about the many strange and wonderful things she had seen on Earth.

LOOK FOR LAURA AT THE WELCOME HOME PARTY AND...

☐ Alien-in-the-box
☐ Baseball cap
☐ Basket
☐ Bone
☐ Candle
☐ Carrot
☐ Cheese
☐ Cupcake
☐ Evergreen tree
☐ Falling stars (7)
☐ Fire hydrant
☐ Football
☐ Graduate
☐ Guitar
☐ Hamburger
☐ Hammer
☐ Hot dog
☐ Ice-cream soda
☐ Light bulb
☐ Meatball
☐ Mouse
☐ Pencils (2)
☐ Rose
☐ Screwdriver
☐ Shovel
☐ Snail
☐ Tent
☐ Turtle
☐ TV set
☐ Unicorn
☐ Yo-yo

From now on, Laura will be very careful when she travels in her astro-ferry.

DETECT DONALD   FIND FRANKIE   SEARCH FOR SUSIE   LOOK FOR LAURA